Debi Gliori
Bedtime Stories

CONTENTS

Little Red Hen

In a little farm cottage at The Back of Beyond lived a pig, a cat, a duck, and The Little Red Hen.

Pig spent his days doing the crossword in the paper, Cat spent her days sleeping and sunbathing, and Duck lounged by the pond making herself beautiful. And Little Red Hen? Well, someone had to do all the work.

Little Red Hen scrubbed, polished, vacuumed, mowed, dug, weeded, shopped, cooked, and did all the laundry from dawn to dusk,

day in, day out, three hundred and sixty-five days a year.

"Where's my newspaper?" said Pig.

"Coming," said Little Red Hen.

"My bed needs making," yawned Cat.

"I'm on my way," said Little
Red Hen.

"I'm starving," moaned Duck.

"I'll put lunch on in a minute,"
said Little Red Hen.

Poor Little Red Hen.

One night Little Red Hen went outside to milk the cows, lay some eggs, and close the greenhouse down for the evening. As she sat milking, she remembered a task that she'd left undone.

"HEAVENS!" she squawked. "I've forgotten to plant the corn. I wonder if my friends would help?"

Back she went into the house.

"I'm a wee bit tired," she said. "Would one of you help me to plant the corn?"

Pig waved his paper. "Not me. I'm stuck on 5 down. Four letters, rhymes with hazy, begins with an 'L'?"

Cat stretched by the fire. "Not me. What a lovely, *lazy* time I'm having..."

Duck looked round from the mirror. "Not me. I've got feathers to preen."

Little Red Hen sighed and went
back outside. She milked the cow,
laid some eggs, shut down the greenhouse,
and then she sowed the corn. By the time
she'd finished, it was nearly morning.

Time passed and the corn ripened. One night Little Red Hen was ironing with the radio on. She heard the weather forecaster say that there was a storm approaching.

"GOOD GRIEF!" she squawked.

"I must harvest the corn before the storm blows it flat. I wonder if my friends would help?"

She opened the sitting room door and poked her head round. "I'm exhausted," she sighed. "Would one of you help me to harvest the corn?"

Pig gave a snort. "Not me. I've just begun another crossword. Listen to this: 2 down, sounds like what a fishmonger does, seven letters?"

Cat hissed at Little Red Hen, "Not me. Don't be so *selfish* – I was nearly asleep."

Duck muttered, "Not me. I have to pluck my duckbrows."

Little Red Hen groaned and headed for the front door. Wearily she picked up a scythe and staggered off to the cornfield. She harvested the corn, put it in sacks in the barn, and finished the ironing. By that time, the sun was streaming in through the kitchen windows, so Little Red Hen didn't bother to go to bed at all.

At six o'clock, she laid four perfect eggs and milked the cows.

At seven o'clock, she watered the plants in the greenhouse and picked four lemons.

At eight o'clock, she cooked breakfast, served it to her friends, and washed up afterwards.

"Toast was a bit too crispy," complained Pig. "Anyone know what 3 down might be? Sounds like sticky, begins with a small green vegetable?"

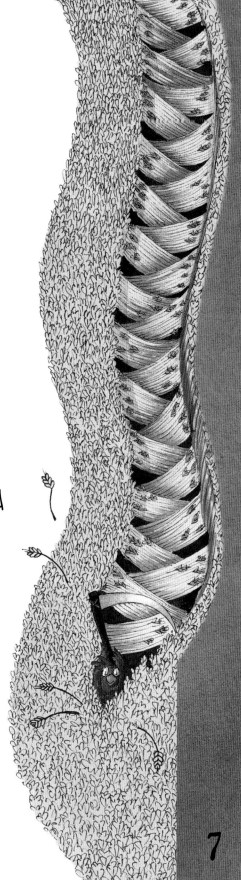

"Call me *picky*," whinged Cat, "but the porridge wasn't exactly up to scrrrratch, was it?"

"I'm still hungry," moaned Duck. "Isn't there any more?"

At nine o'clock, Little Red Hen vacuumed the house, made the beds, and cleaned the bathroom.

At ten o'clock, she polished the silver, dusted the ornaments, and defrosted the fridge.

At eleven o'clock, she collapsed in a chair. "I'm shattered," she whimpered. "Surely my friends will help me out?"

Blinking in the bright sunshine, Little Red Hen dragged herself out to the pond where Pig, Cat, and Duck were draped across deck-chairs.

"I've been up all night," yawned Little Red Hen. "I'm absolutely pooped. Please, would one of you help me make the pastry?"

"Not me," sniggered Cat. "What a liar you are, Hen. I saw you sit down in a chair two minutes ago..."

"Not me," sniffed Duck. "I hate getting my feathers all covered in goop."

Little Red Hen looked at her friends. Something deep inside her snapped.

"Rrrrright!" she said. "I'll do it myself. All of it." And she stalked back into the house.

By twelve o'clock, Little Red Hen had ground the corn, made pastry, squeezed four lemons, made a custard, and beaten egg whites with an energy that she hadn't known she possessed.

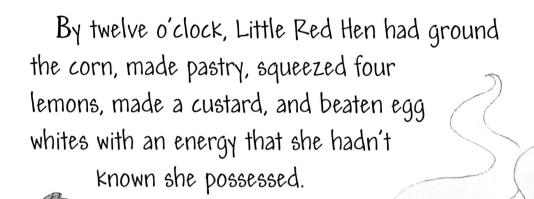

At twelve thirty, she slid a perfect lemon meringue pie out of the oven and onto a plate.

At twelve forty-one and twenty seconds, she appeared at the pond.

"So," she said, dusting her floury feathers on her apron and licking a smear of something off her beak, "who will help me eat my lemon meringue pie?"

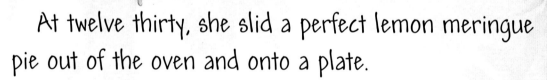

Pig leapt to his feet. His newspaper slid into the pond.

"ME!" he shouted. "I'd be delighted to help!"

Cat sprang to her paws.

"ME!" she miaowed.
"I'll help you right now!"

Duck fell off her deck-chair in her
haste to be first at the house.

"ME!" she squawked. "Although I'd better not eat
too much — it's so bad for the complexion."

"Well, lawks a mussy," drawled Little Red Hen.
"What a helpful bunch my friends all are! But —
what a shame. You wouldn't help me plant the corn.
You wouldn't help me harvest it. You wouldn't help
me make the pastry. I thought you wouldn't help me eat
the lemon meringue pie. So I ate it all by myself.
Without your help. And *mmm mmm,*
it was *deeelicious!*"

The Tortoise and the Hare

"Your get up and go
has got up and gone,"
said the Hare to the Tortoise
one sunny morn.

"Your muscles are saggy,
your rear truly vast;
in the race of the fittest,
I bet you'd come last."

Tortoise gazed at Hare
through ancient gold eyes;
opened his mouth
and digested some flies.

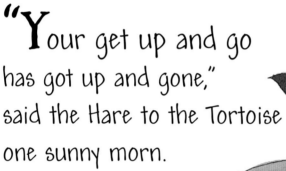

12

"Do I hear a challenge?
A wager? A race?
I'll go get my kit on
if that is the case."

A scant three days later
the Tortoise was dressed;
his tatty old shell-suit
left Hare unimpressed.

Hare looked cool in his trainers,
his shorts, and his vest.
"NOW," he said smugly,
"we'll see who's the best."

"On your marks, get set, GO!"
yelled the Hare,
and straightaway vanished
into thin air.

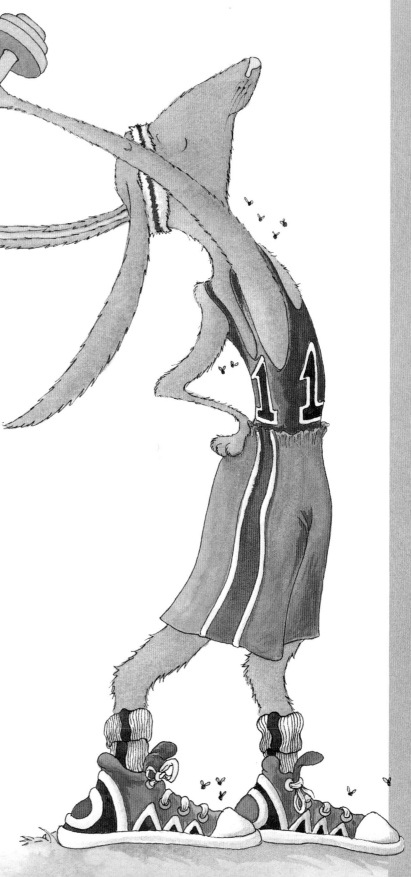

"Ho hum," muttered Tortoise
in an unconcerned fashion,
"I'll just play it cool here –
there's no point in dashing."

One foot after the other
Tortoise plodded on,
pausing occasionally
to stifle a yawn.

Admiring the daisies,
enjoying the view,
taking time out for pit-stops
and going for a poo.

Three light years away
on a far distant star,
Hare shrieked to a standstill
thinking, "I've gone too far."

14

"But aren't I the greatest –
what panache, what aplomb.
What a drag though that I am
now so far from home."

Hare turned around
and retraced his path.
"I'll still win this race,"
he said with a laugh.

Meanwhile... here is Tortoise
just taking his time;
his beady eyes fixed
on the finishing line.

"Slow and steady will win,
not speedy and flash.
The plodder prevails over
the somewhat slapdash."

But what's that up ahead
with long floppy ears?
Tortoise's hunch is
it'll all end in tears.

Hare sets his alarm
for just forty winks.
"I'll snooze, then wake up
and still win," he thinks.

But Hare's sneaky plan
goes badly adrift;
when he wakes one day later
he's seriously miffed.

"Oh how could I be so
completely inept?
Tortoise won the race
while I overslept."

16

Hare had slept through the ringing,
the bells and the chimes.
Hare had forty winks,
but *thirty-six* times.

And here is our Tortoise –
The Winner! The Ace!
(For even no-hopers
sometimes win the race.)

The Tortoise being winner
against all the odds
proves that victory lies
in the lap of the gods.

There Was an Old Woman Who Swallowed a Fly

There was an old woman
who swallowed a fly.
She swallowed a fly!
(we don't know why)
Perhaps she'll die...

There was an old woman who swallowed a spider
that wriggled and tickled and squiggled inside her.
She swallowed the spider to catch the fly,
She swallowed a fly! (we don't know why)
Perhaps she'll die...

There was an old woman who swallowed a frog,
a green-spotted frog complete with peat bog.
She swallowed the frog to catch the spider
that wriggled and tickled and squiggled inside her.
She swallowed the spider to catch the fly.
She swallowed a fly! (we don't know why)
Perhaps she'll die...

There was an old woman who swallowed a trout
that slithered and slipped and tried to swim out.
She swallowed the trout to catch the frog,
a green-spotted frog complete with peat bog.
She swallowed the frog to catch the spider
that wriggled and tickled and squiggled inside her.
She swallowed the spider to catch the fly.
She swallowed a fly!
(we don't know why)
Perhaps she'll die...

There was an old woman who swallowed a swan
so pale and so quiet and so terribly wan.
She swallowed the swan to catch the trout
that slithered and slipped and tried to swim out.
She swallowed the trout to catch the frog,
a green-spotted frog complete with peat bog.
She swallowed the frog to catch the spider
that wriggled and tickled and squiggled inside her.
She swallowed the spider to catch the fly.
She swallowed a fly! (we don't know why)
Perhaps she'll die...

There was an old woman who swallowed a fox
in a little red coat and little white socks.
She swallowed the fox to catch the swan
so pale and so quiet and so terribly wan.
She swallowed the swan to catch the trout
that slithered and slipped and tried to swim out.
She swallowed the trout to catch the frog,
a green-spotted frog complete with peat bog.
She swallowed the frog to catch the spider
that wriggled and tickled and squiggled inside her.
She swallowed the spider to catch the fly.
     She swallowed a fly! (we don't know why)
       Perhaps she'll die...

There was an old woman who swallowed a bear.
Because of his claws, she had to take care.
She swallowed the bear to catch the fox
in a little red coat and
little white socks.
She swallowed the fox to
catch the swan
so pale and so quiet and
so terribly wan.
She swallowed the swan to catch the trout
that slithered and slipped and tried to swim out.
She swallowed the trout to catch the frog,
a green-spotted frog complete with peat bog.
She swallowed the frog to catch the spider
that wriggled and tickled and squiggled inside her.
She swallowed the spider to catch the fly.
She swallowed a fly! (now we'll never know why)
Perhaps she'll die...

There was an old woman who had just one question:
"Oh what can I take to cure indigestion?"
There was an old woman who swallowed a pill.
She swallowed the pill to stop feeling ill.
The pill was a horse-pill, she soon felt
much worse.
Then she died, of course.

24